ROBIN HOOD
A YORKSHIRE MAN

Brian Lewis

BRITON PRESS

1994

Published by BRITON PRESS 17 Linden Terrace,
Pontefract WF8 4AE Telephone 0977 - 793121

Typesetting: Tony Lumb
Publishing Support: Reini Schühle
Secretarial Support: Margaret Morton
Cover Design: Kevin Reynolds and Brian Lewis
Commissioned photographs: Frank Waude
Photography: Kevin Hatfield and Anna Turner

ISBN 0 9520439 5 5

INTRODUCTION

Anyone living in the North today is aware of the debate about whether Robin Hood and Little John came from Yorkshire or from Nottinghamshire. In the fourteenth century there was no dispute, he was a Yorkshire man.

The legend of a Sherwood Robin Hood grew slowly at first but from the sixteenth century onwards, when writers penned more and more ballads to Robin, and Nottinghamshire sprouted archways, dales, wells, caves, farms, hills, larders and meadows all prefixed with the outlaw's name, the advocacy of an alternative homeland for the outlaw was eventually regarded as a mild eccentricity. "Robin was a Nottinghamshire man," the orthodox cried, "and don't you forget it." Of course there were always Yorkshire historians - Ralph Thorsby in the nineteenth century is the best known - who continued to speak up for the other tradition, but they were a minority. People had swallowed the Nottinghamshire public relations exercise hook, line and sinker.

In the 1970s historians looked anew at the question and almost without exception said that Robin Hood was a Yorkshire outlaw. They drew a distinction between a figure who had lived, a historical Robin, and a fictional one. The historical one lived in woodland between Pontefract and Doncaster, the fictional one came from Sherwood.

The two accounts which follow here, called *The Facts* and *The Fantasy*, speak out for the man of substance who was long known as Robin Hood of Barnsdale. *The Facts* advances the case for a historical figure by setting out the documentary and topographical evidence. *The Fantasy* is a panegyric to Yorkshire and a tribute to those Nottinghamshire parochial historians who, having few facts to go on, blow them up into a monstrous legend.

The trouble with writing partisan history - and which historian does not? - is that you can be drawn into shallow cul-de-sacs and yet believe that you have moved onto a historical motorway. Knowing this I have tried to avoid excess and although I will recognise in myself the desire to make the principal villain the Shire Reeve of Knottingley, I know that such romantic excursions are excessive and need to be resisted. What I have not resisted, however, is a very challenging idea. It is that the historical Robin Hood was different from the fictional one and whereas the latter comes with undisputed Nottinghamshire connections there is a sound case which locates the historical figure exclusively in Wentbridge and its immediate environs.

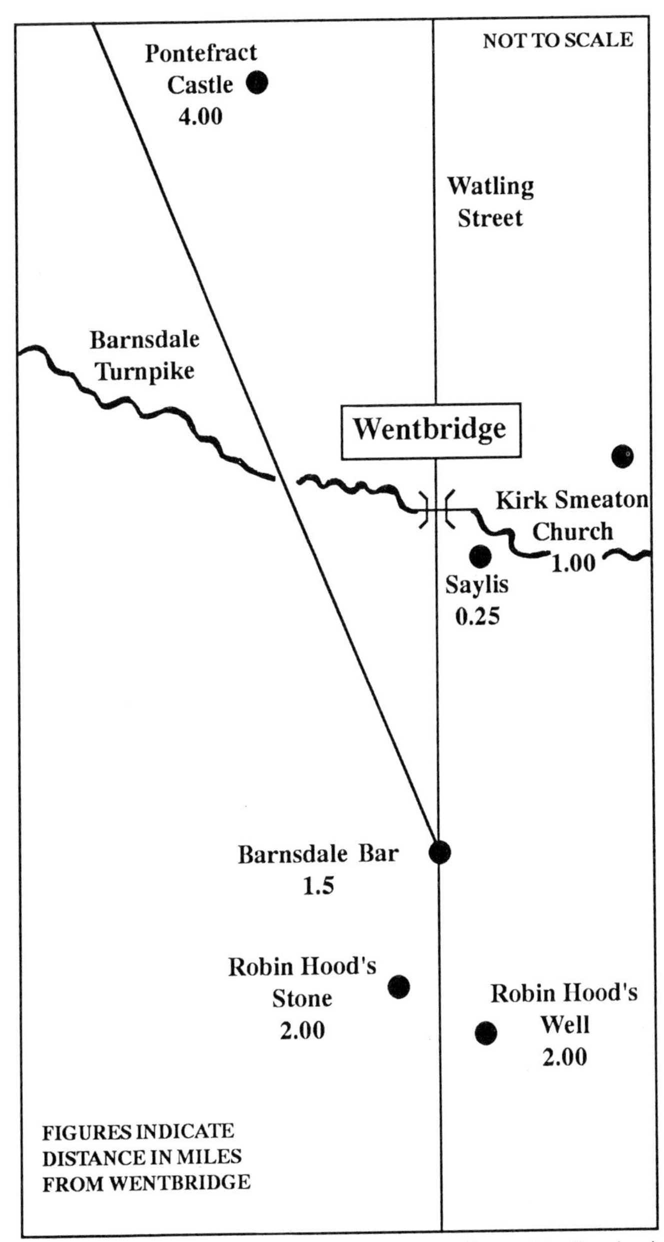

Places mentioned in the text

The Wentbridge blue plaque

THE FACTS

One thing that everyone who has ever looked at the subject seriously agrees on is that there is no way that Robin Hood could have been a Nottinghamshire man. Eminent historians, notably Professor J. C. Holt and John Bellamy, make it clear that the best case for a historical Robin Hood rests on a few brief facts found in the earliest Robin Hood ballad *A Gest of Robyn Hode*. The rest is speculation.

This ballad comes down to us as a very early printed book. It was printed some time between 1492 and 1534 by an associate of William Caxton, called Wynkyn de Worde. It has 456 four line verses, is in eight sections or fyttes and tells how Robin Hood befriends a knight who he meets in the forest, the problems that knight has in paying a debt to the Abbey of St Mary's, York, Robin's battles with a Sheriff of Nottingham, his meeting with King Edward and finally his death at the hand of the Abbess of Kirklees. The story is interesting for a number of reasons. It is clearly based on a much earlier oral tradition and in addition to the main story line presents information about Robin Hood and the location of his adventures which is especially interesting to people who look for a Yorkshire hero.

Of course there are other ballads, later ones written to appeal to an audience thirsty for new stories but this one is the first and has an antiquity which reaches even further back in time. The story line is interesting but it is in the colouring of the piece, and especially place names, that the fascination lies. *The Gest* makes three related geographical points. The first is that Robin Hood lives in Barnsdale. The second is that the outlaw's lookout point oversees Watling Street and the third, and this is most significant, that the lookout spot is called Saylis. Find a

Saylis on high ground overlooking Watling Street somewhere in woodland called the Forest of Barnsdale and you have one very, very precise clue to the historical whereabouts of Robin Hood.

The village of Wentbridge lies in a steep valley, four miles south of Pontefract. Today it is a quiet retreat for retired people and professionals. Little traffic passes through. Pontefract people who want to get to Doncaster, yet avoid the A1(M), use it but by and large few cars pass through. It is a village you travel to for a wedding. One of the best hotels in the area is located there and the Bell is a stylish pub. The young motor there, adulterers meet in Wentbridge for a quiet rendezvous but most of the drinkers are husbands taking wives for a night out.

The quietness of the modern village belies its history. Until the early 1960s, when a bypass road was built, Wentbridge was on the Great North Road and anyone wishing to move north or south through the eastern zone of England, without having to cross the Humber, came through Wentbridge. It was a traditional route. The road had been there since the Romans and was the way north in medieval times. In every respect the topography was well established. Wentbridge lay in a hollow on what was a very old road system.

Anyone travelling this stretch of the road thirty years ago was struck by both the steepness and the unexpectedness of this valley. A driver moving from Ferrybridge south in those days before the bypass was built travelled a road which wandered through gently undulating countryside. To the east there was the vast flat plain of the Vale of York and to the west, sweeping fields leading to the horizon. Then a couple of miles from Darrington the road entered a cutting and dipped, sharply, with a wide bend, to a bridge. This was the bridge of the Went, the structure which gave the village its name. The village - such as it was in those days - was dominated, as it is today, by the Wentbridge Hotel, but there was also a petrol station, a post office, lodging houses, a cafe and a general purpose shop. In those days the cottages on the left hand side were dirty, begrimed by lorry traffic. This was a main road and the houses came right onto the pavement. Thirty years ago they had not been Spanishified with serious white paint and dinky shutters. They took the brunt of the exhaust fumes and dirt sent out from lorries which one way travelled to London and the other to Edinburgh.

In the early 1960s the incline to the north was steep enough but that to the south was treacherous. Icy conditions, and complete rows of lorries would grind to a halt there. This hill has always been a difficult one. It was then, and it was in the time of Robin Hood when it was called Watling Street, as well as The Great North Road. Travellers have always had to slow down at this point. That makes it an excellent place to waylay and steal. This does not of itself make it the place where the outlaws waylaid the knight, it is just a difficult patch of road - until you realise the high land overlooking this bridging point is called Saylis. When in the *Gest of Robyn Hode* the outlaw tells Lytell John, Scarlok and Much, the myller's son, to

Walke up to the Saylis
And so to Watling Street
And wayte after some unleth gest
Up chaunce ye may them mete

he is telling them to go up to a point which overlooks a motorway today and has overlooked a main road since Roman times. There is no such precise and convincing information about a Nottinghamshire location, the location is vital in the case for a Yorkshire Robin Hood.

The opening line of the verse is itself interesting. The injunction "walk up" to Saylis suggests that Robin Hood's camp was in the Went Valley. If it was, then this is exactly where you might expect an outlaw's encampment to be situated. Even today this is a lush valley. By the time the Went has found a determined form as it reaches the bridge it is a fordable stream about ten feet across; a barrier, though not much of a barrier, to a traveller coming down into the valley. The presence of a stream ensured both fresh water and fish; the river plain and the Brockadale Wood - the wood of badgers - , ample wild life. This is a natural place for a village and also for an encampment. It has, and had, everything. When Robin Hood asks the threadbare Knight to eat they enjoy the innards (noumbles) of deer, swan, pheasant, river fowl and small birds. This is exactly the sort of food a valley such as this could provide. The area which surrounds the Major Oak in Nottinghamshire is also lush but there is no comparable stream, no impediment to travellers, no Saylis, no Watling Street and it isn't in the forest of Barnsdale.

It is also important to see that the area just to the south of Pontefract, and including this valley, had a reputation for banditry at precisely the time when historians say the historical Robin Hood lived. In 1307, for instance, the Bishop of St Andrews, travelling south through the area, increased his retinue by twelve extra bodyguards when he got to Ferrybridge. He dispersed with them when he moved through Sherwood.

The Nottinghamshire tourist people make a lot of Robin Hood living in Sherwood and today produce brochures calling on people to come to Robin Hood's County, yet none of the early Robin Hood references set him in their royal forest; all early references to the outlaw place him in Bernysdaile, Bernesdale or, in its modern

Looking down on Wentbridge from Saylis

spelling, the Barnsdale Forest, a small tract of woodland forty miles north of Nottingham. In the seventh line of *A Gest of Robyn Hode*, the reader is told that

Robyn stode in Bernesdale
And lenyd him to a tree

In the early ballads we are not told anything about Sherwood oaks.

The Forest of Barnsdale's northern edge reached up to Pontefract. Today Barnsdale does not exist as a major map reference - forests rarely do - but it does exist in the name of a junction. A mile after passing Robin Hood's Well the A639 leaves the dual carriageway of the A1(M) and branches off to Pontefract. On all maps this is referred to as Barnsdale Bar. This is because it was the site of a 19th century toll bar and as such of interest to early map makers and travellers. Its interest however predates that. This is the point where the medieval road north forked into its two branches. One led north via Pontefract and Boroughbridge to Scotland, the other, via Wentbridge, Ferrybridge, Sherburn-in-Elmet, to York. An outlaw located close to such a junction had pickings from both routes. Across the fields, less than two miles away, lies Wentbridge.

Reference to Robin Hood living in Barnsdale came from very early times. The early focus of interest in the Robin Hood stories occurs in the fourteenth century but by the fifteenth the Norfolk grandee Sir John Paston, in one of his letters, talks about a servant he had employed who had "gone into Barnsdale to play St George, Robin Hood and the Sheriff of Nottingham." This letter is dated somewhere in the region of 1475. By any standards Barnsdale is an obscure forest. You need only to compare it with Sherwood, Arden or New Forest to see that it is in an altogether smaller league. Since it is a feature in a landscape which has no fixed perimeters - medieval landscape references lack our determined precisions - it is difficult to give it a boundary but generous interpretation would not take it beyond the River Aire at Ferrybridge to the north or the Doncaster to Wakefield Road to the south. A line from Ackworth to Pontefract would form the western border and to the east it would stop when it reached Thorne wastes. Its north-south axis cannot ever have been much more than ten miles.

In the Middle Ages, as now, there were few villages in this area and those that there were were small: Skelbrooke, Hampole, Wentbridge, Norton, Campsall, Kirk Smeaton and Darrington. Up to the age of the motor car and commuting, the complete area cannot have contained more than two thousand people and even today its population is small. Yet it was, and is, an area of relative prosperity, for the soil is fruitful. In the medieval period it was just a tract of countryside between two major civic centres, Pontefract and Doncaster. This is not an urban area; not Capone's Chicago or the Kray Brothers' East End, but a quiet countryside area not demanding special interest, yet this is the very area where writer after writer locates Robin Hood. Indeed, the references are so constant and numerous that one is bound to ask: if Robin Hood didn't live in Barnsdale why do the references come up time and time again and from so many sources; from squire's letters, from Scottish Chronicles, from lawsuits and in the writings of England's earliest travellers, which locate him in such a precise patch of Yorkshire.

In a later ballad, *Robin Hood and Guy of Gisborne*, Robin, disguised as the Knight, releases Little John from the Sheriff's house in Nottingham. If you want to look at it from the opposition camp this then is part of the Nottinghamshire tradition of ballad making but for all that it is made very clear that Robin is a Yorkshire man. In this poem the hero introduces himself to the knight as "Robin Hood of Barnsdale". In earlier stanzas of the poem Little John is said to go to "Barnsdale", a place whose roadways he knows "eche one". The place name Barnsdale reverberates through all the early ballads.

If the case for a Yorkshire Robin Hood is so strong, why then has Robin Hood become associated with Nottinghamshire? This is easily explained, for the *Gest* is peppered with references to Nottingham, as are the later ballads, and for this reason the idea of a romantic Midlands outlaw has caught the imagination of Nottinghamshire people. This is understandable, everyone needs heroes and heroines, but it has its negative side.

One of the greatest compliments which can be paid to truth is the suppression of evidence and right up to the present day the Midlanders have been keen to diminish the Yorkshire case and underplay Robin of Barnsdale. Currently there are two Nottingham shrines to Robin Hood; the very popular one close to The Major Oak at Edwinstowe, near Mansfield, and the one in Nottingham itself. The former gives a rag bag of information on the information boards. Robin Hood is constantly described as an outlaw living in Sherwood. The Edwinstowe centre is pure kitsch, a jumble. Friar Tuck hides up a plaster tree, Crusader kings greet Robin, and Maid Marion swans happily through the forest. What makes it memorable is the walk along shale pathways to the Major Oak. By any standards this tree is a remarkable botanical feature. It is a bloated oak of considerable girth which still sends out fresh leaves and is universally admired. Yet further inspection shows it to be held together on well concealed crutches. Planted when Queen Elizabeth was a girl, and therefore two hundred years too late to be a meeting place for Robin Hood's band, it survives as a strong symbol for the Nottinghamshire tradition. There is no truth there but a lot of ill concealed, well managed bolts and underpinning. Of course there is a case for linking Robin Hood with Nottinghamshire but only through fiction, through the dates of books printed from the middle and late sixteenth century. The case for a Sherwood connection comes with the flowering of the legend when Maid Marion is imported from French literature to provide what we would today call romantic interest. That is when Robin Hood begins to reside in Sherwood. When the Robin in the ballad is crude and close to the people, when he is a historical figure, then he lives in Barnsdale and is a Yorkshireman.

It can also be argued that Nottinghamshire plays up its Robin Hood connection because as a county it has few natural assets; it has no dales, no wolds, no medieval city like York, no spas like Harrogate, no major cultural centres like Leeds, Sheffield and Bradford. Compared with Warwickshire it is a disappointment, though placed alongside Northamptonshire it is exciting enough. It is a county which has little to offer, except D H Lawrence, and consequently it has worked hard to make the Robin Hood legend its own.

Yet for all that hard work at one time it lapsed. In 1987 the city commissioned a serious paper on the relationship of Robin Hood to the county of Nottinghamshire. The eminent Cambridge medievalist Professor Holt was asked to comment and to the embarrassment of the tourist people he came up with the conclusion that in historical terms alone Robin Hood's connection was very slight indeed. This pronouncement caused a furore. As often happens in local government one department didn't know what was happening in another and this pronouncement that Robin Hood was in effect from Yorkshire produced a reaction. The council was in uproar. In the late 1980s it was hard enough getting the economy moving but to have a Yorkshire fifth column sabotaging tourism was too much. The paper was immediately withdrawn and heads rolled. It was as if someone had proven that Joan didn't come from Arc or Mickey Mouse wasn't from Disneyland. This lapse, however, did have its funny side. Wakefield Economic Development, for instance, dressed a young member of staff as a Maid Marion and delivered her plus an actor and a local writer of doggerel, to Radio Nottingham where the Sheriff was asked embarrassing questions and challenged to write a ballad supporting the city's case. Then, to celebrate the occasion, Wakefield MDC sited a blue "Robin Hood lived here" plaque on Wentbridge Bridge and came as close as local government will to a genteel guffaw.

As often happens in these cases, the complete issue drifted away but it was lively enough while it lasted. It was a bit of midsummer fun but underlying the joke was a serious historical point. There never was, never could be, a historical Robin Hood who lived or worked in or near Nottingham.

Of course it is impossible to precisely date a historical Robin Hood. Attempts have been made to do so but no one has succeeded. Hood is a common enough medieval name as is Robin. Just as every John Smith reference does not lead us to the Scottish Labour politician or to clandestine weekends in Brighton, not every Robin Hood reference brings us to the medieval outlaw. Yet a number of men of this name can be found in West Yorkshire. A Robin Hood can be located in a medieval tax list and another in a Wakefield law case but this does not mean that we have stumbled across the outlaw or know his approximate date of birth.

The Major Oak, Edwinstowe, Nottinghamshire

On the other hand, lack of any precision does not mean that there wasn't a flesh-and-bone Robin Hood; that Robin was a fairy king or a wood sprite as some writers claim. All it means is that there is no way that you can tie him in with a set of political events. He might have been a deserter from the troops who fought at the Battle of Boroughbridge (1332) or a Wakefield property owner. Such cases have been made. What is hard to dispute is that an outlaw of that name worked out from Barnsdale. To argue against that proposition is to argue against a mass of varied primary evidence and ultimately to argue against common sense.

The case for a Barnsdale Robin Hood is strengthened if we also bring the village name Wentbridge into the equation. There is no mention of Wentbridge in the *Gest of Robyn Hode* but the bridge at Wentbridge is a key element in another early Robin Hood poem, the *Ballad of Robin Hood and the Potter*. In this ballad the outlaw demands payment for passing over the bridge.

Then there are geographical locations with which to link Robin Hood with the Wentbridge/Pontefract area. A traveller moving south down the A1(M) will notice close to the motorway a classical canopy which today seems to have no real purpose. This is Robin Hood's Well and was designed by the playwright architect Vanbrugh in the early eighteenth century on the site of a spring. The history of this Yorkshire site in Robin Hood literature is a long one. Nottingham's cherished Robin Hood's Well, where distinguished eighteenth century travellers saw his supposed chair, bow and slippers, is mentioned in documents as early as July 1500, but the Yorkshire site predates it by almost eighty years. In 1422, in a land related document, the monks of Monkbretton, Barnsley, make use of Robin Hood's stone as a boundary marker. This is close to the well but on the other side of the motorway. Since tenure has to be a precise science around which there can be little arguments, and markers have to be both well known and established, this document suggests a much earlier date for the origins of the stone's name.

Of course there are references to Nottingham and to the Sheriff of Nottingham in the *Gest* but the prevailing impression of the early ballads is that Robin Hood lived in Barnsdale and made occasional trips fifty miles south into Nottinghamshire. There is however a more radical possibility and that is that the historical Robin Hood did not go into Nottingham at all; that there was no historical Sheriff of Nottingham but that the poets and purveyors of the early legend speak of a Nottingham connection for reasons of political expediency and not for reasons of historical accuracy.

At first sight the idea that there was no Sheriff of Nottingham in the history of the living, breathing, Robin Hood seems preposterous; for common knowledge proclaims in essentials that these are the stories of Robin Hood and the Sheriff of Nottingham. Robin is the hero, the Sheriff the villain. It is a traditional formula; left versus right, good opposing evil, thesis and antithesis. Of course no one doubts that that is the formula. Yet formulae are not always neat and tidy. What if the text is distorted and fact faces fiction, flesh and blood faces symbol? What if, in all essentials, we have a historical hero confronting a fictitious villain; a villain who has no historical existence but is only a pasteboard figure made up of all those elements which an audience anxious to hear of Robin's exploits would have him oppose? The problem lies in the variables. The conflict might be constant but the opposing forces might be very different from what we currently allow them to be. In the story of the origins of the Robin Hood legend

High kitsch at the Nottinghamshire Robin Hood Centre

fact may not be opposed by fact, symbol by symbol, but a fact - a historical Robin Hood - opposed by a symbolic Sheriff.

If we express the story as a formula then we have an outlaw confronting the law; or to express the case using slightly different words, an anti-authority figure in conflict with an authority one. Up until now we have been led to believe that this could be directly translated as Robin Hood fighting against the Sheriff of Nottingham; and just because there is a good case for a historical Robin, there must be a good one for a historical Sheriff. This need not be the case.

The case for a living, as distinct from a fictional, Robin is sound; all the evidence of precise locations, Saylis, Watling Street, Wentbridge and the forest of Barnsdale, point to that conclusion. The case for a historical Sheriff lacks all the qualifications which make Robin Hood's case so good. Argue that there never was a Sheriff of Nottingham who opposed Robin Hood and, rather than weakening historical authenticity, you strengthen it. Get rid of the Sheriff and with him Nottingham, and you off-load a number of the problems which make it difficult to bring the historical Robin Hood into a coherent setting. Get rid of Nottingham, and you can, for instance, rid the debate of the somewhat tedious arguments which explain that Nottingham's Sheriff would have some authority in Yorkshire. You also tighten up the narrative by drawing the rural settings close to the urban ones. The outlaw's camp ceases to be fifty miles north of the town of Nottingham.

Anyone who reads the ballads with an interest in historical accuracy recognises that when Robin sallies from the Greenwood there is the sense that he is only travelling a short distance. If Barnsdale is fixed, as it clearly is, then by no stretch of the imagination can Nottingham be at its borders. High Birnham Wood would indeed have come to Dunsinane for that to happen. Even with the modern motorway system the Midland town is an hour's drive from West Yorkshire; in those days, with horses travelling on inadequate tracks, the journey would take a day at least and probably much longer. From this it follows that Robin Hood could not be a historical outlaw and have the scenes of his major urban exploits fifty miles away.

This argument is sound but the best argument remains the cultural one and relates to the way the poem was written. Even today when some authors, probably the majority, write fiction based on fact they modify names. A respectable town like Featherstone becomes Coaltown, Hardy's Sussex becomes Wessex. Authors realise that to call a place or a person by his/her proper name might cause offence, and as a consequence alter it. Since this is done when the slander will be slight we should recognise that it is of necessity bound to happen when the slander is extremely dangerous. A medieval author, especially a non-noble one, could get into serious trouble if he used the names of real lords and their seats of power. Chaucer might get away with speaking out but then he was related by marriage to the powerful Lancastrian lord John of Gaunt. Lesser men would not. A writer without influence only speaks the truth if protected by a lord; then his invective can be gross for he functions as a hack under patronage and not as a true voice expressing popular sentiment. A Nottinghamshire poet singing the praises of of a Nottinghamshire Robin Hood would find it hard to attack a Nottinghamshire grandee.

The case for not having a flesh and blood Midland lord is further strengthened if we look at the character of the Sheriff.

In the earliest ballads he is a cypher, someone who moves the action along but has no personality. The Sheriff is just an authority figure, a shadow. This is what you might expect for if you attack an authority figure in the fourteenth century then best not attack one who is close at hand, who when he hears what you have been singing about comes and gets you. Under such circumstances poets see that it is best not to make the villain recognisable. Locate him somewhere, have him coming from a real place, because that is the normal mode in a vernacular ballad, but one which is not too close at hand. Fourteenth century society wasn't a liberal state in which you could parody or libel someone in power; it was a police state in which notions of free speech were alien to government. In such a situation best have an authority figure who lives over the county boundary and has nothing to do with the House of Lancaster or the House of York. A ballad maker who wants to remain free and intact invents a villain who is remote, a Sheriff from the town of Nottingham, a real town but one a long way off from those you know. The poet who wrote the *Gest of Robyn Hode* knows Pontefract and Doncaster so he lets the lord be a Nottingham lord. Yorkshire people have a developed enmity for Midlanders, it all fits together.

Take this idea on board and a historical connection with Nottingham is removed at a stroke. Nottingham is not a real place, it is just a symbol for a seat of power; the Sheriff is not a historical figure, he is just a symbol for a powerful lord. There never was a historical Robin Hood Sheriff, he is a complete abstraction and a device within a tested literary formula. Every hero must have a villain, the Sheriff of Nottingham is Robin Hood's.

Yet Robin Hood does visit towns and if Nottingham is not his town, what is the town that an outlaw living in

Barnsdale is likely to have known best? The answer is simple, it is Pontefract. Pontefract is four miles north west and closer by ten miles than either Wakefield, a hot favourite in the search for the historical Robin Hood, or Doncaster.

In the fourteenth century Pontefract was at the peak of its national importance. A De Lacy heiress had placed the town and castle squarely within the power bloc of the House of Lancaster. South Yorkshire and the bulk of the East and West Ridings - Sandal Castle, Wakefield was the exception - were to stand a century later for the red rose but in the early fourteenth century they stood for the Barons against the King Edward II.

Edward II was an unbusinesslike king caught up in the act of defending a weak monarchy against a narrow oligarchy of barons led by Thomas Earl of Lancaster, Lord of Pontefract. In this wrestling for power the barons used parliament to advance their own demands whereas Edward II saw the advantage of bringing behind him the merchant and yeoman class - the class to which *The Gest* is politically dedicated - as opposition to these overweening Lords.

In 1322, in the Parliament of York, Edward caused to be enacted a law which henceforth ensured that no statute was valid unless the Commons agreed to it. Through this statute he caused to be enshrined in the British constitution a principle which is fundamental to our basic law. Of course this does not make him a democrat, all he was doing was strengthening his own power base, but it may help explain why the Robin Hood of *The Gest*, ever popular with the yeoman class, remains loyal to this particular Edward.

A major event of Edward's reign was acted out in Pontefract. This was the town from which the king's troops sallied forth to fight the Battle of Boroughbridge and to which the defeated Duke of Lancaster was brought back in chains to be tried and eventually executed. The overwrought imagination might put Robin Hood in the crowd who saw this great lord seated on a mare, an old hat on his head, led to a hill on the outskirts of the town, forced to kneel facing his ally Scotland before having his head severed from his body. One crowd threw pellets of dirt at him while others rushed to his grave, which according to chroniclers was oozing saintly blood, and worshipped his memory.

There is some evidence to link Robin Hood with this turbulent period in Pontefract's history. It is known, for instance, that King Edward was in the area for the trial of Lancaster. The Elizabethan historian Leland, obviously relying on earlier sources, says that the king came with the Despensers to the town and the rebel was brought to him to be tried. In the *Gest* King Edward is in the Knaresborough area, at Plumpton Park, when he decides to dress up as a monk and travel to see Robin Hood for himself. The juxtaposition of these two pieces of evidence, one from the writings of a chronicler, the other from the writer of the *Gest*, again brings the action into the Barnsdale-with-Pontefract area. Again, if we accept these locations, then Robin Hood's zone of operation becomes smaller and more manageable. For Robin Hood and his band of seven score men to have cleared the forest of deer makes sense if the writer of the *Gest* is speaking of an area which stretches from Plumpton south to Barnsdale, about twenty five miles. To clear out a well stocked king's forest, such as Sherwood, would be an altogether different matter.

Accept Robin Hood's location as the forest of Barnsdale and the town called Nottingham as really being Pontefract, and the area in which Robin Hood operates shrinks to manageable geographical proportions. The historical case becomes tighter. The *Gest* says that

Half a yere dwelled our comly kyne
In Nottingham, and well more.......

In the early 1320s during the suppression of the Lancastrian lords and the execution of Thomas Earl of Lancaster, Edward was living in Pontefract Castle for a considerable length of time but not in Nottingham.

The case for a tight geographical location is further strengthened if we take into the case the argument that Robin might have died, and presumably is buried, close to Wentbridge.The final section of the *Gest of Robyn Hode,* which tells of his death, is fragmentary. In 24 lines we are told that Robin Hood decides to visit his kinswoman, the Prioress of Kyrkesly so that she can let blood. Unbeknown to the outlaw the Prioress is the mistress of Sir Roger of Donkaster and these two decide to murder him.

This piece is interesting because if we again argue for a specific location, and seek to bring the setting of the poem into the Went Valley then a case can be made to show that the traditional interpretation that Robin Hood travelled to Huddersfield when he wanted medical treatment is questionable. Two lovers, his kinswoman, the Prioress of Kyrkesly, and Sir Roger of Donkaster, plot his death and murder him when he goes *"to be leten blode"*.

Of the two protagonists the knight is clearly a local. Doncaster lies less than ten miles to the south east of Wentbridge. In the present tradition the woman lives 30 miles away. If the Prioress was from Kirklees Priory, Huddersfield, then this produces problems. Common sense makes us ask, why should a knight travel forty miles to Kirklees, at least a day's hard riding, to meet his lover?

Today, I am sure, Wentbridge men have love nests much further away but then they have cars and motorways. Measured in our terms the distance to Kirklees Priory should be the equivalent of a man travelling to Exeter to see his girl friend. Of course it happens but not too often, and when they meet I should think that modern lovers have better things to do than plot to kill their kinsfolk. Follow this argument and you are forced to ask if it is possible that the location of Kyrkesly is mistaken, and that the church mentioned in the *Gest* is not Kirklees, Huddersfield, at all.

The meaning of a place name such as Kirklees leaves little room for ambiguity. In the 14th century place names were tied to descriptions and this one simply means the church close to the water meadow. Kirklees, Huddersfield, overlooks meadows in the upper Calder Valley. The church which overlooks the water meadows of the lower Went Valley is the Kirk Smeaton church. If we imagine that the poem, and through it the historical Robin Hood, is linked to a number of locations within a radius of six miles of Wentbridge, then Kirk Smeaton is where he died. Pontefract presumably has the cross from which his outlawry was proclaimed and Kirk Smeaton has his grave.

To make sense of the story of the death of Robin Hood it is not necessary to wander too far abroad; the narrative can be contained within the Went Valley and its environs.

Of course, if you start running this way, picking up every fag end reference on offer, you could end up with the Sheriff of Nottingham becoming the Shire Reeve of Knottingley, and show that Sherwood was the scrub land surrounding Sherwood Hall, a manor no more than six miles from Wentbridge near Eggborough. Place name references exist for this Sherwood in 1175, 1202 and 1352 but to try to link these references to the historical Robin Hood is clearly nonsense. Yet the historical case for a Nottingham Robin Hood rests on little more than such fragments.

The case for a Nottinghamshire Robin Hood has few advantages. All that can be said in its defence is that it is a remarkable case of hype triumphing over facts and a recognition of the maxim that if you repeat something often enough almost everyone comes to believe it. The case for the historical Yorkshire is in every sense stronger than Nottingham's case. Barnsdale, Watling Street, Wentbridge, Saylis and Robin Hood's Stone have long histories and what is more, the Yorkshire case is supported by the eminent medieval historian Professor J.C. Holt and all of modern Robin Hood scholars.

Kirk Smeaton church

THE FANTASY

It would have been more appropriate if a badger had pushed up the Mary Magdalene pilgrim's medal which led us to the positive evidence that Robin Hood was a Pontefract man but it was a mole. Brockadale Wood meant the wood of badgers but they had gone to the baitings generations ago leaving the wood to an assortment of wild life and lovers. It was one of the latter, wandering the wood, who had spotted the rectangle of metal on top of the mole hill and taken it home. At first Tracy had wanted Kevin to buff it up at work so she could wear it on a thin golden chain around her throat, but her father had persuaded her to show it to a teacher at the Labour Club, who in turn had suggested that she approach the curator of the town's museum.

Roland Penn had a passing interest in Robin Hood. You couldn't be a museum man in a northern town without getting to know the bare bones of the story. This legend and that of King Arthur caught the imagination of all the town's history buffs and a few of its deranged. Some believed that the Holy Grail was buried under Tesco's, others that St Thomas of Lancaster had recently re-appeared and was conducting a number of miracle cures upon the Airedale Estate but those who showed an interest in Robin Hood at least had some firm ground to stand on.

The case for Robin being a Yorkshire man goes something like this: forget the alternative culture people who want him to be a Forest God, forget those beavers who believe that a name on a Poll Tax return or Pipe Roll can be linked to the outlaw, and concentrate on the man who has come down to us in a series of popular ballads. What do we know about the Robin Hood of the ballads? Well, according to the fifteenth century *A Gest of Robyn*

Hode he came from Barnsdale, had a lookout at Saylis in Wentbridge, and got his men to waylay travellers who rode on the Watling Street. There is little more to know. Saylis, Watling Street and Barnsdale were a neat little patch of Yorkshire, close to Pontefract.

Roland Penn knew all this but he also knew that when Robin returned to the Greenwood he built a small chapel in Barnsdale dedicated to Mary Magdalene. And now, below Saylis, close to Watling Street, two hundred yards from Wentbridge in the midst of Barnsdale, Tracy Bullock, looking for some moss on which to lie on a May morning with her Kevin, had found a medal to that very saint.

His first inclination was to dip into the very small acquisitions budget, press a few pounds into her manicured fist, see her off, and then get a small brush and, in the smallest of small writing, paint a number on the back of the badge. This done he could file the medal in a plastic container where it would be found by his successor thirty years later. This is what they would have instructed him to do if he had contacted Wakefield. Had he done this the tourist map of England would have remained approximately what it was when Edward VII ascended the throne.

Perhaps the White Witches of Brighouse were right after all and Robin was a mischievous sprite, for at that very moment unannounced into the room came one of the handful of people in the town who was historian enough to make the connection. As was his custom, or should it be affectation, Christopher Possitt sat down unannounced and put his calves on an adjacent chair.

"Hello Roland, hello love. How's your dad? I've not seen him at the club recently."

"Tracy has brought in this," Roland said, passing over the medallion, "I think it's medieval."

Christopher needed the name Tracy, otherwise she would have been 'love' forever. On sexist grounds he disapproved of this mode of address but excused it in himself because, though inaccurate and patronising, it was a normal mode of address in Pontefract. He therefore used Tracy twice when he next addressed her. He needed to burn her name into his brain in his fight against middle age. This was preoccupying him, not what Roland was saying.

"What are you here for Tracy? Do you know Tracy, Roland?"

"I brought this thing to Mr Penn. I found it down in Wentbridge Wood; least ways me and Kevin did."

Although the town had a population of 30,000 she saw no reason why everybody in it should not know who Kevin was. After all Kevin was related to Vivian Nicholson, the woman who won the pools and then said that she would "Spend! Spend! Spend!" Kevin's family was famous, so the fact that he was with her when she found the medallion gave her story credence. "We were looking about" (actually they were looking for Kevin's underpants) "when we found it underneath the A1 Viaduct."

"Let's have a look."

He held it in the palm of his hand. "Christ," he said, "it's a pilgrim medal."

Priests get defrocked when they lose faith but what do you do to historians who become so disillusioned with their subject that they regard amateur historians as crackpots and all professional ones as academic fly-by nights? Christopher Possitt was not that but he was someone who had taken Henry Ford's "History is bunk" saying very much to heart.

"Tracy love, if this is what I think it is then you have just brought us the object which will bring prosperity back to Pontefract. You, and Kevin of course, have solved our unemployment problem single handed. My, those are nasty bruises on your neck."

After such a speech there was little to say so she simply opened her mouth, wrinkled her nose and murmured,

"You what?"

Of all of the aspects of the Robin Hood legend the one which gets least attention is the outlaw's veneration for Mary Magdalene. This is partly because up to now Robin Hood has been a children's hero. But since children have grown more adult and adults more childlike it was natural that a shift would occur; that people would start to look seriously at this feature of the legend and go a little beyond Errol Flynn and Richard Todd. Mary Magdalene, after all, is a very modern sort of saint. Faced with a page of dense headlines most men will choose those which include phrases such as "vice-girl", "submission", "massage-parlour" and the like. Mary did the lot. A reformed call-girl - although exactly how she was called is not clear - she came to Jesus, massaged his feet in oil and ended up weeping at the foot of the cross carrying the flask of aromatic ointments to anoint her dead Lord's body. Mary Magdalene had a very modern ring about her and that is why Christopher Possitt liked her and could see a place for her in this strategy to make Pontefract the tourist capital of the North.

The allegiance between the Children of God, a level-headed museum curator and a cynical historian with an eye for the main chance was not premeditated but when the Christian Workshop came into the Town with a golden tent and started to preach a return to an evangelicalism, it took place. The Children of God's arrival coincided with a weekend by the English Civil War Society (Northern Chapter) so anyone choosing to visit their tent on that Friday night to sing *I am H.A.P.P.Y., Sunshine Corner It Is Very Fine* and *God Will Get Us To Mars* was confronted by bearded patriarchs in broad brimmed hats and leather tunics with slashed sleeves. The Civil War Society loved a sing - song with other social deviants - and the Evangelists were deviant enough for most occasions - and had joined in the spirit of cleansing and renewal which was the hallmark of the Golden Tent Crusade of Christian Workshops. The knowledge that they all shopped from trolleys in Tesco's did not distract from the general effect. When he entered the tent Christopher Possitt thought he had wandered into a congregation of seventeenth century Anabaptists who were anxious to discuss what is meant by "Justice" rather than a clutch of Harrogate dentists who were incapable of discussing anything more complicated than the comparative merits of Theakston's and Newcastle Brown Ale. Yet for all that the setting, rather than distracting from the issue under consideration, enhanced it. Predestination was a seventeenth century theme and as he put his ideas to Luke-For-The-Lord, Vicar General of the Christian Workshop, Christopher Possitt came to believe that things were falling out so pat that all was predestined.

Later as they sat together in the tent annex, Christopher Possitt put the case fairly and squarely.

"What I would like you to do, your Worship, is to preach a sermon saying that although most saints are Papist and therefore terribly corrupting, Mary Magdalene is different. She is a direct companion of Jesus and not one of these Italians who gets martyred on a Catherine wheel. You might, I suppose, hint at a physical relationship between them. Jesus was God-made-man, and men spend a lot of time thinking about nubile young women. If you could hint at a direct experience in Brockadale Wood, so much the better. Jesus, after all, did come to England."

Normally the Reverend Luke would not have found it necessary to listen to anyone, least of all a Pontefract propagandist; today he welcomed it. Athough no one else knew it, Luke was in the sort of trouble from which he could only extricate himself with very smart footwork. Two nights previously he had been discovered wrestling, very convincingly, with the devil in a parked van at the Granada Service Station, Ferrybridge. The night time manageress, having seen the vehicle shake, banged on its doors so vigorously that they shot open. She saw enough to convince her that this was not the sort of thing that could be tolerated on a respectable parking lot. Of course she did not know his little pink bum but she did know his face. "I've seen you, you dirty bugger," she said, "you are on those tent posters." He was in real trouble. Therefore, rather than showing Possitt the flap Luke said,

"Yes, I've always wanted to preach on the Magdalene. Jesus obviously had a keen sexual side to his personality and I'm sure that Mary was both his sister-in-Christ and his mistress."

They talked a little longer but in the end he agreed to preach. If the timing in this sermon was correct, Luke reckoned that with the minimum of luck he could hold at least half of his flock and quickly burn away rumours and the memory of Granada's night time manageress.

On the face of it Possitt's advice was sound but the effect on his congregation was not quite as he would have predicted. Unfortunately for Luke-For-The-Lord, though not for anyone else, the tone was not quite right. Initially it looked as if he would get away with it, and convince his congregation that fornication was a holy purgative, but

Pontefract Buttercross - the site of the cross at which Robin Hood's outlawry was proclaimed.

when explaining the evangelical nature of Mary Magdalene's ministry he allowed the word "missionary" to touch the word "position". An audible "Christ" was followed by a giggle and quickly the tent dissolved in uproar. It was too much for the congregation. Although they did not come to scoff and remain to pray, even these strictest of Strict Baptists could not help falling about in laughter. From that time on Golden Tent evangelism had no part on the religious life of Pontefract, or indeed, of Castleford.

It did, however, have one effect. It pushed Mary Magdalene onto the front page of the tabloids and produced the ripple wave onto which Possitt could jump with some skill. The press and television came to Pontefract to see a bonking parson but when they went away England knew that Robin's outlawry had been proclaimed from St Oswald's Cross, now the Buttercross, and that the town Museum had in its possession the love token, a small lead medallion, which Robin had given to Maid Marion prior to their marriage at Campsall Church.

Where did this leave Nottingham? Well, not in a good position at all because increasingly the world came to know what reputable scholars had known for a long time: that the historical Robin Hood's links with the Midland City were tenuous to say the very least. Let us push the problem a little further and ask: Where did this leave the Sheriff of Nottingham? It left him very angry indeed and therefore in the best tradition of the worst Robin Hood movies he began to chunter. The Master of Fitzwilliam, Cambridge, brought in by the council to give credence to the Midland case, was summarily dismissed as a council consultant for hinting that the case for the Nottinghamshire Robin was less than good; and for compounding the felony by publishing this historical controversy, a principal officer in Tourism moved sideways to Parks where he had the job of allotting allotments. When thwarted the Sheriff of Nottingham could be a cruel and ruthless man; but then of course it's what is expected of the Sheriff of Nottingham. Robin Hood was vital for Nottingham's economy and admiration for the rogue went deep.

Front page articles in the *Pontefract and Castleford Express* were taken up by the *Sun* and *Independent* and quickly the culture of the small northern town began to shift. The decision to replace Karl Marx's image at the centre of the Prince of Wales, Pontefract's colliery banner, with a picture of the outlaw posed in the manner of Kitchener and bearing the legend "Your Country Needs You. Fight The Poll Tax" shows that the reclamation of Robin Hood as a Yorkshireman also reached deep into society. Any snub to the idea of a Nottingham Robin became popular. Nottingham was where the Great Strike of 1984/5 was lost and Nottingham's miners were blamed for the closure of dozens of pits between Pontefract and Barnsley. Nottinghamshire was Roben's "promised land", as well as Robin's, so the chance to damage the county in any way was extremely popular. To Socialist school teachers, Nottingham was "that insignificant county to the right of Leicestershire" but this was a genteel response. Rabbie Miller, speaking in a rich Ayrshire accent, and arguing for non-payment of Community Service charges, said emphatically, "There's nought but scabs and whores come out of Nottingham. They're no having our Robin."

Now although there was no way Nottingham could have the Yorkshire Robin, they had put major resources into his promotion and wanted a return on their capital. In Nottingham, especially since the opening of an outlaw centre based on Jorvik, the Robin Hood issue was not

Campsall Church - where Robin Hood married Maid Marion

peripheral but entered the economic development debate as a key issue affecting inward investment.

One would have thought that after Luke-For-The-Lord's veneration for the Mary Magdalene had brought him into so much trouble, he would have sought religious patronage elsewhere. Not a bit of it. The humiliation, which directly derived from his acquaintanceship with the Magdalene, seemed to drive him on not draw him back. Two months after his expulsion from the Baptists he had emerged as an Old Catholic, a member of a church who acknowledged not the apostolic succession of Pope John-Paul II or the Reformation, but found its authority among the Celts who did not accept the Romanist line taken at the Synod of Whitby 663. Accepted as a lay brother by the Bishop of Lesbos, he returned to the Brockadale Valley after his expulsion from the Children of God, with the express intention of building a chapel on the spot where Tracy found the medallion. "Come to the wood, Tracy, and show me exactly where you found the object which has changed all our lives. For I must build a sanctuary for our Brother in Christ."

Tracy answered "You what?", but she went with him, and drawn to his personality she helped him build a chapel.

The chapel in the valley, although it amounted to no more than footings, was stylistically derived from the picket hut architecture of the mid 1980s and had clear advantages as a tourist building. In the first place, had Selby UDC - they owned the wood although Wakefield MDC controlled the main part of Wentbridge - decided to knock down the structure they would have met determined opposition. One does not knock down an English church easily; hippy caravans, the walls of illegally sited green houses, maybe, but churches; hardly ever. The chapel came to be a stopping point on Wakefield MDC's Robin Hood Trail.

"Yes we must take the chapel and its guardian builders into the itinerary" said Christopher Possitt - he now called himself Christopher of Pontefract as he put the case for an expanded tourist programme to the Chair of Economic Development. "When you think of it, Father Luke is ideal. He's in the tradition of the ornamental hermit, a very fashionable figure on the eighteenth century Grand Tour. Chatsworth had one. But he is also close in feeling to Richard Rolle, a very useful figure in our story and someone who could - if Doncaster agrees - also be very nicely fitted into the tour programme."

Most of the points on the Wakefield tour were based on the sort of evidence which Nottinghamshire would have given the Trent for. Their Sheriff's Castle was a rather dull eighteenth century building, housing an equally dull art collection which overlooked nineteenth century dereliction and 1960s office block development downwind of Nottingham's town centre. Pontefract's Castle, by contrast, was a delightful ruin, a natural amphitheatre and the last Royalist Castle to fall in the Civil War. Much of the original stone work was in place.

When it came to describing how to build Pontefract into a tourist strategy Christopher waxed lyrical. "Tourists will start in the refurbished museum by the gates, sample a Pontefract cake or two, and then descend in small parties into the magazine and dungeons to see the graffiti. When they come up they can see a slide and tape spectacular in the barn extensions before going down to see the skeleton of the giant - we'll call him Little John - which was found in the Booths. From there it is on to Brockadale and Saylis, for a walk in the woods, before returning for lavatories - mind we'll have to do something there, most people like modern loos and ours are medieval - the bronze statues of the Merrie Men, and, in the interests of feminism, the Merrie Women. The Buttercross is where Robin Hood's outlawry was proclaimed so we will finish near to the Buttercross, probably at the Robin Hood pump. They could throw coins into the water. That should pay for the lavatory attendant." Anything concerning public lavatories is guaranteed an attentive audience in council briefing meetings. "Any questions?"

"Aye, how much will it cost?"

"Very little comrade; very little, because everything is in place. We just have to make the connection and tell the world that Robin Hood was from Ponte. Nottingham has nothing to compare."

Sixty miles south, Nottingham knew all this was true and therefore its Sheriff, being the responsible public spirited elected member that he was, swore revenge.

Before proceeding, let us ask two simple questions. Number one: was Luke a charlatan, a simpleton, or was he something more?" It is easy to present him as the former; see him as over-pious, over-sexed and over-Wentbridge-way but in doing so we ignore the fact that he built the chapel in the one place in the valley where the Sheriff of Nottingham, or anyone else outside the Ministry of Defence, could not interfere. To have built it exactly under the centre of the viaduct must have been the result of divine intervention because bridges carrying highways are Crown Property which not even Nottingham's Sheriff, however good his Masonic connections, could touch. Three years after the first footings had been sunk, Prince Charles awarded the Cathedral Church and Transport Depot of St Mary Magdalene at Wentbridge (Old Catholic) the Corbusier Award for "listed buildings in modern materials,

Wentbridge Valley from the north

set in areas of outstanding natural beauty." This was when the Sheriff recognised that he would have to accept that Wakefield MDC had hit a six. The night this happened, the Sheriff's wife removed all rush carpeting from the kitchen area of their house in Wollaton. "Just a precaution George; just a precaution," she said tenderly, "You seem so upset tonight."

Number two: was Luke a reincarnation of Richard Rolle of Hampole, or was he, as the gutter press would have us believe, merely a father of four who had abandoned his wife, an outworker at Double Two Shirts, to follow a selfish star? A difficult question, for if you have never heard of this Doncaster hermit you must not count yourself as too ignorant. Richard Rolle is not the sort of figure who crops up in after dinner table talk. A Yorkshireman from Thorton, born 1290, died 1349, and therefore a contemporary of our outlaw, he had gone up - or is it down - to Oxford but left when he was nineteen and set up cell close to the priory at Hampole, a village on the edge of Barnsdale and part of the Doncaster District Council. Today Rolle is remembered as the writer of a number of long poems, both in Latin and the vernacular, which deal with the end of the world, and one in particular which is called somewhat colourfully, *The Prick of Conscience*. Oh yes, and he used to wander the woods dressed in his sister's shift.

"Christ," said Tracy sitting bare-legged, her arms clasped around her knees listening to her hero and watching the sun go down below the Saylis plantation. "Do you mean that this old fellow wrote a book just about his thing? That's disgusting."

But Luke was not listening. "Tracy," he said, in a dreamy voice, "do you mind if I call you Marion?"

So it was that Tracy, now called Marion, left a comfortable home on the Chequerfield Estate, Pontefract, left a house with a computerised washing machine and microwave oven, to live in the Greenwood and to wash her underwear in the murky waters of the Went.

Since Marion and Luke represent the forces of light and the Sheriff the dark adversary, we can easily accommodate them within the traditional boundaries of the Robin Hood legend. They are very clearly romantic figures. Christopher Possitt, in contrast, for all his protestations to the contrary, is not. "This year it's Robin Hood, next year it will be the discovery that The Man In The Iron Mask came from Knottingley," he told Lucy Pilkington, a commentator from the BBC, as they walked the bypasses of Wakefield looking for a road sign which read Pontefract in big letters, and found one with "Elvis Presley is a wanker" in minute pencilled ones.

A fortnight later Lucy came, as any history graduate would, to her conclusions on the television sets of England. "So who was Robin Hood? Was he a robber living in Lady Thatcher's old constituency, who stole from the rich to give to the poor? " (close-up of a man in Mafia glasses, dressed in Lincoln Green standing on a traffic island somewhere in London); "was he the patient of a Kirklees Prioress and her live-in-lover, Roger of Donkaster" (close-up of the founder of the Yorkshire Robin Hood Society dressed as a nun and wearing the sort of crucifix associated with Hammer Films); "or perhaps he came from Sheffield" (a close-up of another young man in doublet and hose standing on a traffic island); "Christopher Possitt , however, reckons that he came from Pontefract."

This statement was followed by a long shot, with voice over, of Lucy and Possitt walking up from the Town

Hall towards Boots the Chemists. For this occasion he wore his reading glasses on the end of his nose, as befits a scholar anxious to present himself to an audience snoozing after dinner.

"I've no doubt he was a Yorkshire man," Possitt said. "In the first place it says so in the earliest ballads and the area has a number of geographical locations, like Robin Hood's Well, which date from very early times. Nottingham has nothing to match either source." This was said with great authority enhanced by the word which flashed across the screen. It read, *Historian.*

"But couldn't he have come from Nottingham? The Sheriff is the Sheriff of Nottingham?" said Lucy doing her continuity bit.

"No, and it is that which proves the point. If the writer had lived in Nottingham he would have called the villain of the piece *The Sheriff*. If you live in a place you don't mention it by name. I'll say of you "Lucy from Toxteth" but your friends in Liverpool will just say "Our Lucy". They know where you are from; they don't have to tag a place onto your name. The fact that he's called the Sheriff of Nottingham establishes the case that the Sheriff is an outsider. Yorkshire was being oppressed by Nottingham, that is why the villain is treated to his full address. Robin Hood, just the name, it's for "our" local lad, but the Sheriff "of Nottingham", for the man who does not belong here."

That was enough for the Sheriff. Although he knew that he was coming next and footage would show him immaculately dressed in his robes of office and that he would soon be seen by millions, travelling to Nottinghamshire's Major Oak in the Civic Rolls Royce, he rose rapidly and switched over to Brookside.

Leaders of Councils, Sheriffs, Prime Ministers do very little themselves because they have others to do things for them and it was some of these others that the Sheriff of Nottingham summoned to his presence at 8.30 am, an unprecedented time, the next morning. "I want," he said, "a strategy to defeat this Wakefield bid. I want it to be sharp, I want it to be good and I want it by this time tomorrow."

Nottingham Council's record, as a taker of major tourist initiatives, was almost as good as its record in media relations. Whereas many councils would have spent weeks passing paper between departments to try to see if this ought to be handled by Planning or Economic Development, Central Administration or Publicity, the Nottingham Officers got down to it immediately. By lunch time a skeleton paper was in existence and at five o'clock it was coming out of the main frame.

The report, when it came, was thorough but it left little room for manoeuvre. They had checked out Possitt; it was right, he was an academic historian. It was true, a medallion had been found. Father Luke was a rogue but that had already been covered in *The Sun* and was yesterday's news. His chapel would probably be listed within the week. The relevant Minister, it seems, was a brother of the Patriarch of Lesbos. They found it difficult to penetrate the Wakefield corridors of power and discover who was handling Robin Hood for the Metropolitan District Council but it was clear that someone was doing some work somewhere. Judged from a historical viewpoint Possitt was right, the Wakefield case was as strong as the Nottingham one was weak. Yes, Yes, Yes, the Castle was medieval and of great potential. Brockadale Wood was beautiful, the people of the Five Towns of Wakefield were

Robin Hood enthusiasts. When he received the report the Sheriff was calmer. He had already decided what to do. You do not become Sheriff of Nottingham without indulging in a bit of ruthlessness. Desperate times require the desperate sort of remedies which would not be approved of by a committee of local government officers. He was Nottingham's "Man-of-Destiny". He would work alone but it would not be easy.

"Wakefield have said that your desire to keep the Robin Hood legend to yourself is the result of your low economic and marketing performance in other fields." It is Sunday night and Dame Valerie Singleton is interviewing the Sheriff for the *Money Programme*. "How do you answer that?"

Although he was used to the new competitiveness which successive Conservative governments have encouraged to develop between one local authority and another, he was growing tired of the tussle with Wakefield; why always Wakefield?

"A lot of things are happening in Nottingham."

"What, Sheriff?"

"Oh, we have a range of diverse small scale industries."

"Wakefield says that whereas their Economic aitch - the M1 and A1(M) linked by the M62 - amounts to the nation's principal area of commercial growth, you offer nothing more than cigarettes, indigestion powders, lace and the type of bicycle used by the Witch of the West in *The Wizard of Oz*."

It is too easy to always present the Sheriff in an unsympathetic light. The title and style of his office are ancient and if, in the popular mind, it has to be occupied by a villain, that is unfortunate. In his way the Sheriff was doing a good job. He was trying to promote his town and wrestle with under-investment and unemployment. In fact, he was merely doing what Wakefield had done at the end of the 1980s, that is before the tide turned and left the South East stranded upon exceptionally polluted beaches and the Midlands in a backwater. His action has to be seen in the light of the prevailing morality and not from the romantic perspective of medieval literature. Nationalism and township chauvinism, ruthlessness in business practise - and petty violence - had been encouraged for twenty years and the Sheriff merely reflected a prevailing political and moral philosophy. It was Wakefield with its emphasis on cooperation and collective unimagination which was out of step. The Sheriff's decision to buy-in MI6 and the SAS, was a natural and imaginative one. In the search for ways to beat unemployment it is every man for himself.

John King - we will use the name he used when introduced to the Sheriff on Ladies' Night at the Ancient Castle Lodge (No 604) - was a specialist in espionage. Recruited at Balliol, blooded in the Royal Navy, trained in Northern Ireland and prepared for undercover work in Russia, he had become obsolete when the Government had abandoned Fortress Britain and recognised that glasnost opened up the Russian market in such a way that there was no point in having a large espionage presence in the USSR. Seeing through to the core-logic of her programme, Lady Thatcher and later John Major encouraged MI6 and the SAS to go freelance. King was an officer who had taken advantage of her generous redundancy and retraining package. His business card read, "Commander John King M.A. (Oxon) - Specialised Plumber."

When King saw the Sheriff's report he agreed with him that there was little point in pussy-footing about with strategies which would take too long to come to fruition. To destroy the tourist problem of the Went Valley and

Pontefract he needed to get his hands on the Mary Magdalene medallion.

Ferrybridge Service Station, like all motorway restaurants in the middle of the night, is a hub of activity. Between 11.00 pm and 2.00 am it is filled with people who, having played the gaming tables in Wakefield and Leeds, retire to sober up on black coffee, gammon and egg. For the next hour the majority of customers are unhappy men talking earnestly to other men's wives. This is also the hour when rugby club stalwarts, for a bet, take a run at the high pitched roof and try to reach the apex. (Thud, thud, thud - "Yes I'll leave her this time; yes I really will.") The next two hours are quiet and it is in this period that the staff get down to essential cleaning. Anyone entering at that time is immediately noticed if only for the simple reason that they are in the way.

A taste for chauffeur-driven cars sneaks up on a man but when established it is hard to throw off. Reckoning that the essential trips of the night, the reconnaissance of the Went Valley and the trip to Pontefract to look at the Museum, would be carried out in King's Maxi veteran motor car, the Sheriff had brought the City Rolls five miles from the target area and parked it on the Knottingley side of the car park and well away from the service station itself. This done, he had wandered in and ordered two pieces of sliced bread, toasted and buttered, to show that he was one of the people. That done he sat there, seemly inconspicuous, awaiting his pick up.

Now although he expected to be unrecognised he wasn't. Anne Caithness, the night manageress, knew immediately who he was. She had seen the Rolls Royce before, but also she knew the man who got out because, unlike the Sheriff, she had watched the end of Lucy

Pilkington's BBC interview. In it the Sheriff had been driven down the leafy lanes of Nottingham, emerged in full regalia - black silks, a flowing gown and a heavy silver chain - to say that although Robin Hood lived in Nottinghamshire six hundred years ago and the theme park's Major Oak was only four hundred years old, it did not amount to an incongruity.

The others in the restaurant also knew the Sheriff. Woo Wing and Lee Yuan Lee had been principals in the Chinese delegation which had rejected Nottingham as a setting for the Great Wall of China Exhibition. The international importance of Wakefield's Economic aitch - the M62 crossing the A1 and the M1- had been quickly recognised by these very men and therefore they had sited the exhibition further north. The mile long replica wall which snaked from junction 32 on the M62 up Glasshoughton's slag heaps, was a reminder of that invigorating time. It was also the first of the number of full scale replicas which we associate with the Pontefract/ Castleford Great Walls site. When the five year festival was over, Mr Woo and Mr Yuan had bought a hall on Heat Common. They still liked to eat at the Granada, Ferrybridge; the food and architecture of the Service Station, they said, reminded them of their childhood in Hong Kong.

"I always find it useful to meet in this type of setting," said King coming through the check-out with a mug of hot chocolate, "the plasticality of it all allows us to merge with the natives." There were six people in the Ferrybridge Service Station at the time.

Like many of his class and experience Commander King believed that foreigners only understood you if you spoke deliberately and in a loud voice. Therefore he took little account of the Chinese and went on to explain the intricacies of his operation in an audible whisper. It was a mistake, for Woo Wing's loyalty to his adopted area was beyond reproach. As he had explained to Pontefract Rotary on the previous Tuesday, a Yorkshireman is not someone who is accidentally born within a perimeter of land but someone who deliberately chooses to adopt an area's values. When the Sheriff and the Commander left to look at Pontefract and Wentbridge, the timing of Operation Long Bow and much of its detail was known to two exceptionally loyal Yorkshiremen.

Tracy, now called Marion, was as usual up early looking for magic mushrooms. Father Luke taught that you could only live outdoors in the summer rain of England if your mind had gone for a spin before breakfast. Hence the early morning ramble. The sort of fungi she sought was usually found down by the river, but this morning she had climbed up to the very Saylis Hill, where six centuries before, Robin had sent Much the Miller's son, Will Scarlok and Little John to look for travellers.

To call Saylis a hill is a trifle misleading. If you come at it from Doncaster along the A1 it is the plateau which precedes the Went Valley but coming at it from the stream as she did, it is very definitely a hill, a steep hill covered in dense undergrowth.

When she accidentally came up behind them, Commander King, dressed in a Gannex macintosh and green Wellingtons, was trying to persuade the Sheriff to fight his way through the briars and nettles and descend to the valley close to the springing of the viaduct, thereby avoiding the traditional pathway opposite the village post office, for, as he said, "The religious nutter and the doxy are camped close to that pathway. Any sort of noise will wake them."

As an expression of Northern hospitality, Tracy would have probably said something like, "God-a-mercy fine sirs; and what brings you to the Greenwood on such a morning" - she and Brother Luke had as their current night time reading the omnibus edition of the *Scripts of Hollywood's Robin Hood* - but she had never heard the Cockney word "doxy" before and its tonal proximity to "poxy" made it seem offensive. Therefore, instead of greeting them she kept her peace and listened.

"It seems to me," King went on, "that this side of the operation is relatively simple. We stake out their lair and then early next Wednesday evening, we photograph them in a compromising position. Then it's up to us. A friendly tabloid will run a "Teenager and Old Vicar in Vice Scandal" lead, or perhaps better still, we can start circulating pictures of the young madame in the buff around their working men's clubs and council estates. We won't come too heavy. Alsatians, I find, make people run so it need not be a hands-on operation. Next day we'll do a bit of crop spraying - I'll arrange for something pretty toxic to fall off the back of a Portman Down lorry - and then it's bombs away. Within the week, we'll circulate rumours of anthrax, blaming the Libyans. They're right, it is a valley of exceptional beauty. It won't be by the end of the month."

Tracy was worried by the imputation that she and her spiritual adviser were carnal lovers. Because she now knew herself to be a Cartesian, "I think therefore I am." She hated the idea that the attack on Luke, herself, and their beliefs would be based on something as sloppy as a fundamental untruth. Tracy slept under the same duvet as Luke, that much was true, but that was because he practised a particular form of asceticism - also practised by the Desert Fathers and by Richard Rolle of Hampole - which encouraged saints to deliberately seek temptation and confront it both face to face and buttock to buttock. "Marion," Luke would say, "it's not really much of a

The River Went

temptation if you are dressed like that. What about something whispy, a Janet Reger bra, a black suspender belt. I might find that encouraging," but Tracy/Marion - what you will - would merely wrinkle her nose, put on another cardigan and draw the bed socks closer up to her knees.

That night as they sat by the fire she told Father Luke what she had heard.

"Why is it," she said, "that the middle aged, obsessed by guilt, seem to wish to transfer their sexual problems to others?"

"Marion, I wish I knew the answer to that. On the other hand this I do know." In the absence of certainty action must take the place of speculative thought." With this he lapsed into an extemporised prayer. "And as we think of our brother in Christ Jean-Paul Sartre let us also give thanks for the life of he, who like us, brought innocent children into woods, to sit by fires and drink cocoa; thy servant Baden Powell, our Lord, Amen."

After he had prayed for a minute in silence, he opened his eyes. "Marion, my child," he said, "we will *Be Prepared.*

Nottingham's attack was to be two pronged; an attack on the museum to be synchronised with one on the camp in the Went Valley. The former was to be led by the Commander, the latter by Jock, Snowy and Big Mick, pit men recruited in the Ollerton area. It would take place at dusk on Wednesday 21 October, Trafalgar Day.

The choice of day, from Nottingham's point of view, was unfortunate. The Old Magistrate's Court in Pontefract's Town Hall is dominated by a bas relief of the Death of Nelson which bears the legend "England expects every man to do his duty." During the 84/85 strike the miners and their families had sat facing it so that it had become something of a talisman. They were the real England, not Nottingham, and their *duty* was to overthrow injustice. Therefore when Father Luke approached Steve Money, the Kellingley National Union of Miner's Branch Secretary, there was already a community of interest. They greeted each other affectionately.

"Now then, old cock."

"Bless you my son."

In Pontefract eccentricities of speech and manner are tolerated.

"How's our Tracy?"

"Nicely thank you. How's Maud?"

"Nicely."

The natural courtesies of civilised life over they got down to business. As an ex-miner invalided out of the industry but with established credentials - Luke could still claim his coal allowance - he was asking the NUM branch to support him. His house was threatened and he wanted a twenty four hour picket to be mounted close to his dwelling. He made it clear that he was not asking this as a favour; it was a formal request to the Branch Committee.

Money, for his part, agreed that there was nothing unusual in the request. The 1984/85 Strike had been about the protection of communities and therefore there were firm precedents for union action. Although he could not give a firm guarantee, he agreed that this was a serious matter, and would have to go in some form to the executive. Both Luke and our Tracy could, he said, count on his support.

Thus it was that three Featherstone Rovers forwards and one Staffordshire Bull Terrier were lurking in the bushes close to Saylis, looking for travellers just as little John, Much and Will Scarlok had done in the *A Gest of Robyn Hode* so many years before.

As fate would have it the three men hired by Commander King were members of the defunct, but once flourishing miners' break-away union, the UDM, and as they made their way through the brambles, down towards Luke's encampment, trailed by a Wapping photographer in yellow shoes, Nosher Norris recognised the man in the lead, "Yon's the bugger who hit me with the shovel at Cresswell during 'strike," he whispered, "I'm bloody sure he is."

"Come on Duck. We want to get there today," Big Mick shouted over his shoulder. These were the last coherent words he uttered before he was taken into Pontefract General Infirmary.

It would be nice to report that Nosher, Clancy and Tim Buck jumped onto the shoulders of the Sheriff's men from the branches of an overhanging oak tree but since the trees in Brockadale are not of this order they made do with a sprint through the trees and hit their adversaries squarely in the manner of a loose scrum. "Here we go, here we go, here we go," they chanted. And so they did. In less than a minute three Nottingham miners were laid out and having their little fingers tied together. When Luke and Tracy came up the Alsatian was nowhere to be seen and the photographer was whimpering by the tree,

Two hours later, night staff coming on duty at the local hospital were confronted by four men tied together and with Elastoplast over their mouths. One of them - the smallest - was dressed in a mini skirt, silk boxer shorts and expensive yellow shoes. So ended the Battle of Brockadale, and just as it did the Battle of Ponte Museum began.

The Keep - Pontefract Castle

No one thought it very unusual when a succession of folk singers and clog dancers appeared in the square in front of the town Museum and facing Supersave. Local arts groups had established this area as a major outdoor venue and since Wakefield MDC had emerged as the nation's only arts-led economy, so the people and traders of Pontefract had come to accept music, outdoor sculpture and performances as something as common as street trading.

King was spotted at 16.36 exactly. Rebecca saw him pass a box of matches to an accomplice in the door step of Argos before making his way into Supersave. Although she had played the opening bars for *Underneath the Lamplight* she never reached *the barrack gates* but instead entered a spirited rendition of *The Theme Music from "The Sting"*. Capable of playing almost anything, her colleagues followed her into the melody but in Supersave Commander King, looking for somewhere to hide when the shop closed, did not even register this change of mood. Of course he would not, his musical education started and finished with the *Dam Busters' March* and *Music From The Last Night Of The Proms*.

In the museum Roland Penn heard the tune and activated the telephone tree. On hearing the opening bars of *Beethoven's Fifth Symphony* coming at them via the services of British Telecom - the closeness of the Menwith Hill tapping service made it inadvisable to use words - the people of Pontefract once again knew where they stood. At the sound members of the Art Club, the Historical Association and the Pontefract Archaeological Society picked up their thermos flasks and moved quietly through Tesco's car park to the museum. Anne Caithness of Granada had done well when she reported the Sheriff's early morning conversation to her museum curator.

Five thirty came and with a "See you in the Ancient Borough, Amanda", "See you in Kiko's, Dawn," the shop girls departed. The shop empty, the Commander came out of the stock cupboard and peered down on the front door of the museum. At five thirty exactly a red Fiat driven by Roland's wife pulled up and he loaded in the day's shopping. He then locked the stout oak door with a large key and drove out from the pedestrian precinct.

Five minutes later, unseen by the Commander and his assistant, he entered the back of the building at the first floor level by the fire escape and quietly took his place alongside the sixty or so citizens who were sitting in a shallow circle facing the door to the stairs.

Only inexperienced burglars go into buildings from the back. People who have thought the problems through look the building in its eye, saunter up and make a frontal assault. In this way the casual observer is not alarmed. So as the Commander came out of the store, locking the door behind him, because he wasn't dressed in a hooped jersey or carried a bag marked "swag", the two people still in the precinct did not seem to notice him. Without hesitation he took the ladder which had been delivered earlier in the day and climbed up to a large circular window; then took a sheet of high adhesive film and a toffee hammer from his pocket. He had practiced and quickly the glass was covered with clear film. With a few smart taps the window caved in and as the Commander crawled in through the round window a car drew up, the ladders were stowed and with no sense of urgency, the car moved away.

Although he had never been in the second of the Museum's store rooms he had studied the building from outside and had guessed correctly. One minute and 17 seconds - five seconds earlier than he had predicted - he was working with skeleton keys on the first of the internal doors.

When he was through that, he would have the door to the stairs, the passage door and finally the complicated one which led into Roland Penn's office. Quite suddenly the lock responded and thirty seconds after he had come through the window the door could be pushed gently open.

He did not expect the scene which confronted him. As he entered the room with habitual briskness, Mr Woo and Mr Yuan, dressed for the occasion in Karate suits with black belts, placed their hands on their thighs and bowed. Then they shot into action. With a cry which sounded like *Ponte* they moved forward and hand-chopped a six inch block of deal. Mr Woo and Mr Yuan were demonstrating loyalty to their home town in a way which struck fear into the Commander.

As he stood rooted to the spot, from her seat in the corner of the room Lucy Pilkington rose, and walked across to the Commander. She smiled and then with a, "Won't you come this way" preceded by Woo Wing and followed by Yuan Lee Yuan, led the secret agent into the Museum's meeting room. Before an invited audience, with BBC cameras panning in and out, she then invited him to put his side of the story.

Lucy's - and indeed the Commander's - timing was perfect. When she made her introductory remarks it was exactly two minutes and two seconds after he had put his foot on the ladder. That night, as we all know, Lucy Pilkington's professionalism was established and her reputation as an investigative journalist made.

What did the ordinary viewer, sitting on the settee with a tray of food, make of it all? What did they take from the programme? Well, of course, some remember the bones of the discussion; remember how an intelligent twenty five year old interviewer so successfully picked the meat off an intelligence officer, that he ended up admitting that deep down he believed that Robin Hood was a Pontefract man but more, perhaps the majority, remember the audience better than they remember the interview. They remember how the middle aged men and women from Pontefract's major historical and art societies, dressed in tweeds or anoraks, seemed not in the least interested in the riveting interview, but throughout ate sandwiches from Tupperware containers and drank tepid tea from plastic cups. Then how, at a prearranged signal, they rose, and in unison, led by a woman in a blouse and royal blue skirt, sang in perfect pitch *There'll Always Be An England.*

The Robin Hood, Pontefract